BRITAIN IN PICTURES
THE BRITISH PEOPLE IN PICTURES

BRITISH FARM STOCK

THOROUGHBRED AYRSHIRE COW

Oil painting by Juliet McLeod, 1947

BRITISH
FARM STOCK

THE EARL OF PORTSMOUTH

WITH
4 PLATES IN COLOUR
AND
33 ILLUSTRATIONS IN
BLACK & WHITE

COLLINS · 14 ST. JAMES'S PLACE · LONDON
MCML

PRODUCED BY
ADPRINT LIMITED LONDON

PRINTED IN GREAT BRITAIN BY
CLARKE & SHERWELL LTD NORTHAMPTON
ON MELLOTEX BOOK PAPER MADE BY
TULLIS RUSSELL & CO LTD MARKINCH SCOTLAND

LIST OF ILLUSTRATIONS

PLATES IN COLOUR

BLACK AND WHITE ILLUSTRATIONS

*The writer's thanks are due to L. B. Powell for his help in delving into records of breed improve-
ment; to H. J. Massingham for advice on the first part of this book; to the Milk Marketing
Board and the Ministry of Agriculture's Statistical Departments for their ready assistance; and
for the help in the selection of illustrations given by Walker's Galleries, through whose courtesy
illustrations on pp. 7, 14, 16, 17, 21, 22, 24, 25, 26, 27, 30, 31, 32, 33, 36, 37 and 39 are reproduced.*

GROUP OF CATTLE
Oil painting by Aske Corbould, 1879

INTRODUCTION

THE THOUGHTFUL TRAVELLER

AT sunset a traveller climbed westwards to the pass above the timber line. At the top of the divide he and his horse paused by mutual consent and looked into infinity falling away from them. Already the deep valleys were in shadow. Below, where timber and pasture began again, the air was full of golden dust where the sheep had been gathered for the night. They were Hampshire Downs, black faces and black feet. Behind the pass, whence he had come, was the registered Hereford herd through which he had spent the earlier hours riding—"white-faces" as the cowboys called them.

Sheep and cattle alike at that moment seemed patriarchal; flocks and herds that might have been guarded by the followers of Abraham and Lot, instead of the Polack shepherd and the native-born, soft-spoken cowhands. Yet they were beasts whose immediate ancestors came from a far island; for they were roughly 1,500 miles south of Hereford and 5,000 miles west of Hampshire; moreover, as the bird soars, a mile and a half nearer to the stars.

How came these animals, bearing the hallmarks of their forebears among the gentle orchard-dotted slopes of the Welsh marches and the

7

'THE TREK': A HERD OF HEREFORDS IN THE ALBERTA FOOTHILLS
Oil painting by Matt Lindstrom

trim folds of rape and turnips below the English Downs, to be foraging
for a living among the sere pastures and fallen timbers of the high Rockies,
and thriving on what they found? How, for that matter, does it happen
that, wherever new worlds are won (and, alas, too often wasted) for plough
and pasture, one finds Shorthorn and Ayrshire, Hereford and Aberdeen
Angus, Hampshire and Ryeland, to name but a few of the great list of

8

animal colonists from Britain and the Channel Isles? True, there are Brown Swiss and Holstein, Merino sheep and the hardy pony descendants of the Conquistadors; also derived breeds like the Rambouillet sheep and the Poland China pig. But, from all the continent of Europe, excepting for some notable breeds of chicken, little else has left its mark upon the animal husbandry of Africa, Australasia or the Americas. Asia has only excelled in its desert horses and camels. The animal blood of the small United Kingdom has been as outstanding as its human blood in its passage across high range, prairie, bush and forest.

From tropical highlands in Africa or Brazil to the winter-fast steppes of Canada they flourish, these British breeds of livestock. They seem as adaptable to climate and conditions as the men who bred them in the British Isles.

Justly to describe the breeds of these Islands, and their origin through the influence of soil and farming, merits years of deep research and many volumes. This small monograph, in which it is only possible to deal with a selection of the more famous or remarkable British breeds, can only attempt to interest, as much by picture as by prose, those many who have been too much engaged in other pursuits to have had the time or cause to ponder over the history of British livestock.

There are fifteen separate breeds of horses and ponies, twenty-four breeds of cattle, thirty-three breeds of sheep and twelve breeds of pigs indigenous to these Islands. These indeed are the principal recognised separate breeds, but they by no means include the whole tale of individual inherent characterisation in our animals. Thus it is clear that, even were it desirable, it is not possible here to write a dictionary of national farm-animal biography. Rather will it be necessary to consider why British livestock has achieved its position; the influence of livestock on our history and on men; the influence of history and men on our livestock; and in so doing to draw examples from the different races and their breeders.

THE INTERACTING INFLUENCE
OF SOIL, CLIMATE, HUSBANDRY AND MEN

WHILE it seems likely that our climate was once more extreme in heat and cold than it is to-day, it has probably always been equable enough for hardy flocks and herds to survive bitter winters and an occasional droughty summer. Animals and men had to be capable of constant adaptation to wind and rain, sun, snow and sleet and to changes of temperature that might vary many degrees in a few hours. The plants likewise on which they subsisted had to be equally adaptable and hardy. The great point is, that the climate made for hardiness, but rarely was it so severe that stamina and all other characteristics had to be evolved merely for survival. For instance, cattle of Africa and Asia evolved humps on which to live in times of drought, but they yield only a few miserable pints of milk in good conditions. Yet there are mediæval British records showing that good cows averaged over 400 gallons of milk a year without winter fodder crops, and suckled their own calves as well. Therefore it was a climate blest in the fact that, even with primitive fodder conservation, cattle could survive the run of most years round.

The second influence on our livestock is that, compared with parts of Europe like Brandenburg or Castile, there is no poor soil. It varies infinitely, but there is hardly any land in Britain which does not yield fair sustenance. Moreover, for centuries the population of the whole of England was less than a tenth of what it is to-day. Except for reasons of defence, there was only need to cultivate the better acres of our land. The great monastic orders, which were often pioneers of good farming, chose the fat lands which still yield best to-day. Thus while flocks and herds had much ado to shift through the long winter on their little meadow hay, their range was wide and their soil was good. Here the woodlands helped cattle and pigs to no small degree: pannage meant rooting, acorn and beechmast for the pig, stray grasses, young shoots and ivy for the cattle. It is still within living memory of some in Wales that old men rode through the winter woods cutting down ivy from the trees with a long hook and then sounded their horns to summon the village cattle to the feast.

Climate and soil and a small population, which nevertheless lived almost entirely by agriculture, all favoured livestock husbandry. Moreover, livestock meant more than food. Boots, clothes, tillage, transport and even military policy were dependent on animals.

Save for glory, the horse was little used. Tillage depended on oxen, and the hide (a measurement of land) was supposed to be based on a plough team's work. Transport was by pack-mule. The "S" curve of the road outside many a village is the result of the pack-mules winding between the headlands of the common fields. Mule, jennet and donkey were the most common riding animal. Hence in the main the horse was the knight's charger and was bred to carry his heavy accoutrement. This breed probably was the father of our heavy work horses of to-day. Except in passing, breeds of horses are outside the scope of this book, for they have been the subject of a book already published in this series. Though ten breeds of horse were known to the Elizabethans and the "Great Horse" (drawn by Stratanus in 1570) was certainly a draught animal in Shakespeare's time, horses in the Middle Ages, and indeed later, had little part in British farming.

A FARMYARD NEAR HONITON IN DEVON: YOKED OXEN AND HORSES
Wash drawing by Thomas Rowlandson, 1756–1837

In those days communications were difficult. The servants of the King, the great nobles and ecclesiastics were the main travellers. It was part of the royal purpose that many-manored nobles should have holdings widely scattered. Thus, the cloistered self-sufficiency of village life meant that separate types of stock inevitably came into being, and this was fostered also by the very individuality of the men who kept them. It was also dictated by the infinite variety of English soil, geology and climate. While the tradition of the clan, as opposed to feudal organisation, in parts of Scotland and Wales may have had some differing effect on livestock development, yet here again the nature of the hill country itself had a paramount influence on livestock.

> The mountain sheep are sweeter,
> But the valley sheep are fatter;
> We therefore deemed it meeter
> To carry off the latter

wrote Peacock in *The War Song of Dinas Vawr*.

Even now, hill flocks have to be acclimatised to be able to live on their particular mountain. One of the tragedies of the winter of 1947 was the near obliteration of whole flocks acclimatised to their own sheep run. Even had sheep from other districts been available they could not, except by a long process, have replaced the old flocks.

The acclimatised flock is only the extreme example of nature making her own special arrangements. On lands attached to Beaulieu Abbey, two surviving farms are called Bergerie and Vacherie. There is no doubt that sheep and cattle respectively still flourish best on these farms named from their kind. Near Land's End, facing the full Atlantic gales, there runs a shelf of land half-way between the sea and the bouldered hill tops, where a native Guernsey type of cow has established herself and thrives better than all others. Perhaps the most famous of all examples where man and nature have co-operated to make a breed that is eminently suited to its own peculiar environment is the Romney Marsh sheep. Here, because the Marsh could not hold the sheep through the winter, a complementary economy of upland agistment grew up; it resulted in a breed which has dominated the livestock economy of Kent and on account of the protean qualities evolved thrives across the world.

This interchange of stock between highland and lowland, and later between wet west and drier east, has been responsible for some of the fundamental excellence of English stock. Despite the long-continuing difficulty of communication, the variation of soil and climate even in short distances made specialisation in type a much wider affair than would otherwise have been the case. Several qualities rather than a single one were needed. Draught oxen were blood kin to milch cow and beef animal. The wool trade developed from sheep that supplied clothes, mutton and

A DOWNLAND RIDGEWAY
Water colour by William Turner of Oxford, 1789–1862

even milk. The early ancestors of our breeds were notable because, while relatively unimproved, they had many latent qualities from which the great breeders could draw in later centuries.

There is a tendency to dismiss the farming and the stock of mediæval Britain as wholly dark, primitive and dismal and as a consequence to suppose that light only came with improvers in the eighteenth century. This is hard to believe. In fact it is probable that the *average* animal was better then than now. However primitive the three-field system may have been, men lived very close to and utterly depended on their animals. Instinctively they must have recognised the better sire, since they knew their neighbours' stock and the Lord of the Manor's as well as their own. The average farmer did not, as now, buy cattle from market or dealer, with no more knowledge of the animal's family or history than he could have of the tax collector's in Whitehall. The mediæval farmer with this close knowledge must have known that living depended on something more in his byre than

13

"nicely matching roans". Again, stock, men and land interacted as unconscious partners. Man at that time did not feel impelled to prove his conquest of nature. The result was that this partnership with nature formed history, as much as did kings, nobles and ecclesiastics. The great agricultural fairs like Weyhill in Hampshire were established, where sheep in tens of thousands congregated, and hops from Worcestershire and cheeses from all the Western shires found their "alien" market.

In this connection, it was stock which made the "green droves" of England. Through the Midlands and Lincolnshire can still be found great roads mainly running north and south, which are often 75 yards wide. These cattle-droving roads were used to bring beef to London and stores to the lowland farms. Other droves from west to east brought sheep and ponies from Wales. Across the Down tops of Wessex and elsewhere are the wide grass streets like the Icknield Way and the Ridgeway along which sheep were driven and whose origins are lost in the mist of time.

The Neolithic and Bronze Age peoples, for instance, possessed a small, wiry, hair-fleeced sheep which shed its wool and these animals must have been driven along the ridgeways from settlement to settlement.

A HOLDERNESS COW, BRED NEAR MALTON IN YORKSHIRE
Mezzotint by William Ward after George Garrard, 1798

ALDERNEY COWS WITH CALVES
Water colour by Robert Hills, 1769-1844

For the most part the green roads clung to open hills, where surprise by raiders was more difficult. The great Berks-Wilts Ridgeway, for instance, runs just under the Downland summit, the Icknield Way parallel with it just above a line of springs and greensand. Thus the movement of stock influenced the pattern of our landscape. Perhaps it had as much influence as the free movement of stonemasons across the land in giving us that

15

common culture which defied the intense individuality and localism of the Anglo-Saxon. It is interesting that when that great Augustan of English farming, Coke of Norfolk, held his agricultural gatherings, which drew men from all the civilised world, he did not choose the Harvest Home; men came to his sheep-shearings. It was a natural recognition that stock is the pivot of British farming and not the cash crop for sale, even in a great grain country like East Anglia.

Manorial agriculture may have left much to be desired, for its very nature tied men to the pace of the slowest and it inhibited soil improvement. Yet the stock was held by individuals, even though it was pastured in common. Perhaps this accentuated the Englishman's natural aptitudes towards the care and breeding of livestock. The crops were a communal affair almost entirely, in that the farmer never tilled the same strip twice; the animals were what he could make them by breed and management.

One finds stock influencing local customs. In the New Forest it was the enclosures which grew corn, but the common open forest which carried stock. Thus, men had to fence out stock rather than fence it in. From this grew the hardy mongrel cattle of the Forest and the admirable breed of

OXFORD DOWN RAM
Early nineteenth-century water colour by W. Nicholls of Dunstable

Wessex Saddleback pig, which had to be good mothers, good rangers and fatteners. They still are, wherever they are found to-day. The New Forest has taught us many valuable lessons.

The Forest land would not easily support sheep, and only hardy cattle. But if the bramble and holly were to be kept in check, a variety of grazing was needed. Deer and ponies did their part. The Forest commoner might bitterly resent the Royal deer, but when they were thinned almost out of existence the grazing became poorer and only the pony kept back scrub, especially the holly. The small tough ponies played their part on many open heathlands and, for better or worse, it would have been difficult to win our coal without them. Thus the primitive pattern of our agriculture was to help nineteenth-century industries.

However, it was sheep that moulded our commercial beginnings. Every schoolboy knows that the Lord Chancellor sits upon the Woolsack because wool once represented our commercial greatness. Perhaps few realise that it was not built on wool brought from Australia and elsewhere to be woven in Blake's dark satanic mills of Yorkshire. In the early Middle Ages, the English wool went to Europe, especially to the Low Countries; then, as

THREE LEICESTER WETHERS
Water colour by R. Whitford, 1871

17

the power of the monasteries increased, the Kings of England built up her wealth on protected manufacture of the home product, introducing the Flemish weaver to teach the English how to weave the fine cloth in demand across the awakening world. It is a long, not unromantic story of a policy expanding England's trade and possessions on methods which the Manchester school were only able to reverse for one declining century because of the supremacy which it had given us beforehand.

Apart from deliberate policy, one great blow of fate enormously accelerated sheep-keeping in England. The Black Death reduced the population to something like a million and a half souls. At once this made much cultivated land redundant for tillage and almost automatically untied the villein from his soil, despite efforts like the Statute of Labourers to hold him to it. On the other hand, many yeomen and peasants acquired their own land on freehold or copyhold from the depopulated manors. Like so many trends, when increasing rewards are involved, it had abuses which were pilloried in the pages of Langland and from the pulpit of Latimer. Indeed, it marked the beginnings of enclosure and of landless labourers. Yet it is interesting to note that England's commercial and industrial greatness and the foundation of her overseas trade were not laid on coal and iron, but on wool from her own sheep.

The mark was left as deeply on the countryside as on her history. Many of the loveliest Cotswold churches and manor-houses were built on the wool of the Lion breed of sheep, probably first bred by the Cistercian flockmasters. Indeed, there is a notable period of English architecture which, instead of being called Perpendicular, might be called the great wool period. Stokesay Castle was a great wool magnate's country house. The towns and ports which end in "stable" or "staple" are other symbols of that early commercial rise, for it was here that the wool clips were collected.

Naturally, wool comes first to one's mind when thinking of the early history of English livestock but, as we have noticed already, cattle left their pattern too. The long strip was the result of ox-teams' ploughing. The gentle end curve of the strip towards the headlands, which can still be seen in the Midland pastures, was made so that teams could turn more easily at either end. Gradually the trim, disordered pattern of our fields grew up to suit the stockmasters of the time. Our lovely hedgerow timber was a compromise between the need for firewood and building stuff and husbandry for grass and plough. Our water meadows were also made for stock. Our open Downs remained unfenced as sheep-runs, the fertility of which was carried to the lowland folds at night. Even our deep, foxgloved lanes were made to suit our stock. The arts of banking, hedging and stonewalling were decreed by stock. Some think the origin of our earliest parks lay in the cleared open space before the fortified manors or the castle's curtain wall. Here the stock could be brought at the first alarm, so that raiders

AN ENGLISH FARMYARD SCENE
Water colour by Robert Hills, 1810

could be seen before the foray was attempted. The mind of many an exile pictures countryside and village as England in his dreams, or it may be a steep Welsh valley or Highland glen with ruined shielings that lives in his memory. Except for the smoking cities, whatever his rural picture, it was etched in the course of time by livestock on our land.

If livestock has had this physical and commercial importance to us, it has done much to foster character as well. Anglo-Saxon organisation and later the manorial system taught local co-operation; the team spirit grew in the workaday life of the village, which also organised its games and festivals in co-partnership with its work. While much was done in common, the livestock was the individual's care and property, and at night, save for the sheep which were folded on the lord's land, the stock came home to the family cot and orchard close. As all over the world, before the dawn of compulsory education, children learned their first lessons in responsibility by tending animals.

Now it was the combination of a husbandry which pivoted on livestock and yet had need for tillage that really made its mark on our character. Your real stock-keeping nomad thinks only in terms of a day, and moves on, trusting to find fresh pastures on the morrow. He is generous and hospitable as a rule and he may value his mare more than his wife, but he is also cunning, suspicious and destructive, because he is not tied to any field or parish. Often he treats the results of his own folly as the act of God. Perhaps the supreme example of such folly were the hunting parties of Genghis Khan, where game was driven by fire over hundreds of square miles into a small circle for one great massacre. Even the Viking nomads of the sea, once settled, had need of husbandry, and for the rest the conquerors of England were essentially husbandmen. Had this not been the case, the very northern nature of our climate and the woodland character of our land, forbade a nomad life and enjoined settled cultivation.

At the same time, as we have noted, the soil was rich and the pressure of population small. Hence there was no need for the really crabbed serf life to enforce itself. For example, in parts of Europe and Asia, where the soil is poor and could do little more than keep men just alive, little margin remained for animal husbandry; only the goat scavenged and ruined the steep, untillable slope. All of which means a hard, avaricious, unkindly life for soul and body on land that becomes old and worn out. Ours were the Fortunate Isles which allowed us to keep more than enough stock on a system which was both individual and co-operative. The Englishman's then simple needs and his primitive equipment still allowed him a holiday on every Saint's day in the calendar.

It was only with the rise of post-Renaissance commercialism and industry in the seventeenth century that grinding work, real poverty and poor physique began to be endemic in the country. It is probable also that monasteries were a cushion against the privations caused by a succession of bad seasons. Although the people's diet varied much from valley to valley and although they were certainly not enormous meat-eaters like the gentry, the summer abundance of livestock products must have meant a good deal to their physique. History gives us proof of their qualities as soldiers in the field. The slow decline in physique had probably just begun in Elizabeth's days, yet all through that period the striking beauty of the English was remarked upon by travellers. This great building-up of health, stamina and character must have been due in no small part to a livestock husbandry.

A man's fortune was his stock. He needed to protect it from beasts and human enemies, to tend it for his food and clothing. Being almost self-sufficient in his village crafts, cause and effect were never lost to him. Having plenty of leisure which could not be divorced from working life, his whole character and sense of responsibility must have been deeply influenced by animals. He and his team were one on the furrow. Animals run through our literature from the earliest times. From the thirteenth-century "Awe bleteth after Lomb" down to Gray's "The lowing herd wind slowly o'er the lea", and on to our own day, the thread is interwoven. The contemplative peace engendered in the shepherd, or indeed the neat-herd, is proverbial. Sterner qualities too were needed against wild animals; great fortitude and individual responsibility were demanded to save flocks and herds in bitter winter storms. Then there was the final sense of duty which sometimes decreed that the family would have to endure short rations in order to save the animals on which so much depended. In later pages, we will see how these qualities persist into our own times.

DISHLEY RAM: ROBERT BAKEWELL'S IMPROVED LEICESTER BREED
Lithograph from R. W. Dickson's *Practical Agriculture*, 1805

SHORTHORN BULL, 'FAVOURITE', SIRE OF THE FAMOUS 'COMET'
Aquatint by J. C. Stadler after B. Taylor, 1819

FAMOUS BREEDS AND BREEDERS

T HE beginnings of our commercial supremacy lay in the manufacture and sale of British wool. Later opening of the new continents produced a ferment in town and country alike. Consequently there were very few improvements of the eighteenth century not adumbrated by seventeenth- and even sixteenth-century pioneers and writers. But it was not until the pressure of industrial population began in the latter half of the eighteenth century that these improvements became widely developed. As the swelling towns needed food so, for better or worse, commercial farming superseded subsistence farming.

Oxen lingered on surprisingly late in many places, and until very recent years they were in use at Earl Bathurst's farms near Cirencester. But on enclosed fields horses were quicker and more easy to turn than oxen, and thus the great breeds of heavy work horses developed. The small, steep, wet fields of the West produced a lighter type, half-way between the pony and the great Shire horse of the flatter, more open Midlands. These Shire horses were to prove invaluable as heavy dray horses in the towns. The tall, fast-moving Clydesdale proved the best work horse of the North. The flat lands of East Anglia produced the sturdy, short-legged chestnut Suffolk Punch, in many ways the counterpart of the grey and black Percheron and Belgian horses from similar country across the North Sea.

For most of us it is only in the mind's eye that we can see the lovely sight of well-matched plough teams, often three or four at a time turning the land, with gulls wheeling and settling in the furrow's wake. The horsemen who tended them were—those who remain still are—men of rare character, whose pride in and responsibility for their teams were matched by their intimate knowledge of the soil. On every acre which they ploughed, they walked the furrow for many miles and so they knew their soil's character as no tractor driver has a chance to do. Through horses town and country still were linked. Draymen and stablemen needed the country for horses' oats, hay and straw. These latter returned to the neighbouring farm and market garden as good manure for the town's fresh food. What colour, and even music, the great days of the horse provided, from the hunting field to the Whit Monday parades of City horses, with their burnished brasses and plaited straw and ribbons! The wagoner's matched horse-bells were harmonised with an ear to music more subtle than coach or hunting horn. Perhaps it was the horse, from coster pony to the great Shire, which, through all the drab misery of the Industrial Revolution and even later, warded off that dreary proletarian sameness of our pavements.

SHIRE STALLION, 'ENGLAND'S GLORY'
Coloured aquatint by Thomas Sutherland after Thomas Woodward, 1825

MR. JOHN GIBBONS WITH THE LINCOLNSHIRE OX
AND HIS FAVOURITE FIGHTING-COCK IN HYDE PARK
Oil painting by George Stubbs, 1790

Yesterday made macadam and the horse. Our era has independent front-wheel springing and the crawler tractor. Yesterday produced the Norfolk four-course rotation and to-day the predigested, precooked and vitamin-injected food package. But even if eggs are powdered, milk homogenised and meat canned and corned we must return to the eighteenth century to see how this modern feeding of the masses became possible on the soil which is still our source of life.

Until the days of Coke of Norfolk and Turnip Townshend—those great noblemen who would have deserved a Nobel Prize with palms—winter was a time of general scarcity. But turnips made winter meat possible; clover renewed the soil, made better beef and more abundant milk. So it was possible for great breeders to build on foundations where environment was the mortar of heredity. Latent qualities of our stock could not be developed while winter was a season of survival only.

Probably the greatest of all our breeders was Robert Bakewell (1725–95) of Dishley in Leicestershire. He gave us the Leicester sheep. He also bred Longhorn cattle, but with less universal success. Incidentally, he worked with Coke of Norfolk at Holkham for a time. Moreover, he achieved indirect fame through his pupils, Charles and Robert Colling. By careful

LORD SPENCER WITH HIS CHAMPION BULL, 'WISETON'
Coloured lithograph by W. H. Simmons after Richard Ansdell, 1844

selection of Yorkshire Shorthorn types and very close in-breeding, they were the founders of the Shorthorn breed. To prove to neighbours the potentialities of in-breeding, Charles Collings bred his best bull back to his dam and her resulting heifer to her own sire. This produced the famous bull 'Comet', the leading sire of his time. Again, later, Thomas Bates of Kirk Leavington carried the Colling brothers' work towards a more distinct dairy type and Booth, his rival, tended more towards beef. Hence the phrase "Booth for the Butcher and Bates for the Pail."

These early breeders were great artists, who arrived empirically at the principles of genetics. Incidentally, Bates's successors were to learn that in-breeding can only be sound when hereditary taints are absent. Some of his Duchess lines tended towards sterility. Faulty in-breeders towards the end of the nineteenth century found their animals losing constitution.

Meantime, Amos Cruikshank in Aberdeenshire greatly improved the breed of beef Shorthorns and developed a fine export trade from Sittyton to the Americas. George Coates published the first volume of the *Shorthorn Herd Book* in 1822 and thus the most universal breed in Britain got its

official start. Even in Tudor times the Earls and Dukes of Northumberland bred short-horned cattle and it was from Teesdale that most of the dual-purpose Shorthorns were developed later by the great Yorkshire breeders.

The Eastern counties produced the Red Poll, one of the oldest types in Europe, perhaps 8,000 years old. A tenant from the Holkham estate, John Reeve, crossed the Norfolk and Suffolk types, to found the breed as we now know it. Apart from its dual-purpose qualities and general longevity, its hornless quality is most interesting to-day, for the hornless animal is more docile to manage and saves superficial horn injuries. So much is this the case that dairy farmers are beginning to dehorn their cows, and in America a polled (that is, a naturally hornless) breed of Ayrshire is being developed. The hornless inheritance is genetically dominant and so is very valuable when polled types are required. Red Polls have, by crossing, quickly removed the five-foot horns of the Ankole cattle of East Africa.

Another polled breed came from Scotland—the Aberdeen Angus. This is a beef breed *par excellence*, with its quick maturity and close meat on light bones. Once again it was the result of intense in-breeding. Scottish meat is probably the best in the world and the great Scottish breeders were mostly beef men, for Scotland produced the Galloways (also polled) and Belted Galloways, the latter a bovine edition of the Wessex Saddleback pig in colouring (i.e. black with a white belt towards the shoulder). The shaggy-coated Highland cattle are also full of good beef characteristics, as well as picturesque qualities for the Landseer school of painters.

Southward, the Hereford is probably the widest-spread of all our beef breeds, the sires of which have fetched great prices for export. But the Duke of Bedford persuaded Coke of Norfolk to adopt the sweet red Devon breed as winter feeders in Norfolk, a choice that still holds good in many cornland farms of East and Southern England.

At Holkham the famous sheep-shearings became the forerunners of our modern Agricultural Shows. They were more, because they fore-shadowed our modern farm walks, where neighbour farmers learn from each other's methods and criticise stock and crops. The shearings, usually lasting three days, included exhibitions of livestock, judging carcases, sale of ewes, letting of rams to tenants, awarding prizes for making water meadows, visits to neighbouring farms, exhibitions of threshing machines and other implements.

PRIZE RED POLL BULL, COW AND HEIFER
Oil painting by an unknown artist, 1851

26

THOMAS COKE, M.P., WITH SOME OF HIS SOUTHDOWN SHEEP AT HOLKHAM
Coloured mezzotint by William Ward after Thomas Weaver, 1808

Listen to the *Norfolk Courier* of 1804:

"Mr. Coke's hospitable and extensive mansion at Holkham, and every inn and farmhouse in the neighbourhood, were filled with visitors. Those who had never before visited this part of the kingdom could not suppress their admiration at the high state of cultivation into which so very large a tract of land, naturally sterile and barren, has been brought, and at the very fine and thriving plantations which are raising on land which naturally produced not a tree of any kind, but was, till within a few years past, a vast plain of chalk covered only by a few inches of sand, so extremely light that it shifted and blew about like new fallen snow, with every wind."

Coke of Norfolk was one of the widest and most artistic minds of his time. The countryside of his creation, his buildings, his learning, his collection of pictures, his political interests—all attest his many-sided genius. But he was only *primus inter pares*. His contemporaries were artists in life, as well as farmers; for breeding is using the knowledge of life. For instance, the improvements wrought by the great Lord Townshend were all done in something like six years. Although he was most concerned with cultivation, his achievements in so short a space of time would be an agricultural

27

miracle even in an age of specialists and big machines. It was this ability to perceive nature and select from inherently sound stock bred over the centuries which gave British breeders their impetus in the eighteenth century. Incidentally, the great place which British livestock held over the turn of the eighteenth century is shown in the many portraits of famous animals by artists from the great George Stubbs and Morland to Sartorius and Ferneley.

At last the roast beef of Old England was here to stay for nearly a century and to linger until 1939. The mutton came too. The Southdown strain permeated all the short-woolled Down breeds that were evolved by turnip, rape and clover. Here again great artists in breeding arose and developments of hybrid sheep between hill and plain began their commercial course. While each breed came into being because of local soil and climate, their vigour as hybrids became known where they could be crossed to obtain stamina and early maturity among the lowland farmers, who needed soil consolidation and fertility. The great breeders tried out their rams by hiring to other farmers, as did some of the early bull-breeders. Thus it was possible to test results on a very wide scale without losing sight of sires which might become great proven getters in their old age.

Some sheep like Leicesters and Border Leicesters, Southdown, Romney Marsh, Suffolk and Hampshire Downs and others seemed to possess great qualities for adaptation in other districts. Many breeds were suited best to the local conditions; these still remain of practical value to-day, not only for home use but for fattening and crossing elsewhere: thus the Dorset Horn, with a potential of two lamb crops a year, the Clun, the Kerry Hill and many other breeds.

In the '70's, the heyday of arable farming, there were over 28 million sheep in England. Although their number has dropped sadly in the great corn-growing counties, we still have the greatest number of sheep per acre of any country in the world, namely about $14\frac{1}{4}$ million all told (Dec. 1948).

Sheep, indeed, were the pivot of farming in many lowland counties up to 1914. It was the sheep which had the best hay and the shepherd was almost monarch of the farm, as other departments knew all too well. The pulse of the farming year beat to the occasions of the flock. In the great Down counties, the familiar sight of the lambing fold told the passing of the winter solstice. The little ovine thatched town, that was built with straw walls and lean-to straw roofs, had individual lying-in wards for the ewes. At that period the shepherd was not only king of the farm, but the immanent patron saint to his flock, some of whose lambs would grace all too soon the Easter Sunday table.

If the sheep relied on the shepherd, the land relied on the sheep. Their little sharp hooves gave the light soils a consolidation better than any roller for future crops. The manure from their folds would grow next autumn's wheat, or this spring's barley. Often the sheep would graze on the Downs

BLACKFACED SHEEP
Water colour by Birket Foster, 1825–1899

and the sound of sheep-bells would be heard in the evening as they came back to their folds on the arable land, bringing the upland fertility with them.

In the late spring came the sheep-shearing; more than welcome to the farmer whose whole season's expenses had come to a head before he could hope for harvest. The wool cheque was balm in Gilead. Then there were the great sheep fairs where many tens of thousands were penned, frequently to go to those farmers who only carried a flying (fattening) flock to bring fertility, and to deck the butcher's shop window. Some of the sheep and generally the rams were "reddled", that is, their fleeces were coloured with ochre, a practice pleasing to the eye which still prevails in certain breeds. Even twenty years ago, a sheep fair like Stockbridge Fair brought to life a chapter out of Dickens, with the wide old single street filled with characters of an almost unimaginable richness of variety in clothes, speech, manners and idiosyncrasy. For many it was a bitter moment when "Canterbury lamb" (frozen lamb from New Zealand) could be hawked at 2*d*. a lb. in the streets of Southampton, and all security went for the sheep farmer until, too late, Hitler caused us to guarantee prices a year ahead for the unborn lamb.

29

This is a picture of the arable counties, but wherever there were hills in the north and west of England, sheep were not only the pivot of the farm: they were the farm itself, and that is true even to-day.

The hill farms produced another breed of livestock, varying with the district. This was the collie and the sheep-dog. Although the lowland shepherd always uses a dog, there is never the same intense cultivation of the dog that often has the brain and always the legs of half a dozen men. On the hills the sheep-dog is the shepherd's seven-league boot. Thus it came about that not the least picturesque part of rural life are the sheep-dog trials on the Border, in the Dales of Yorkshire and many other hill districts; trials which enthral the experts and almost bemuse the holiday spectator by the understanding between master and dog and the latter's superhuman skill. Incidentally, the little Corgi, so popular to-day as a pet, was developed for herding the black Welsh cattle of the hills.

In hill farming the weather is always hazardous (in the hard winter of 1946–47 it is reckoned that about four million sheep were lost); and so sheep and shepherds become almost Biblical and symbolic, for the parables of the Bible are as true to-day as they were in Palestine two thousand years ago.

And this brings us via the prodigal son to our pigs. It is significant that the prodigal son could live with his pigs, for the pig is a naturally clean liver and about as omnivorous as his master. In Ireland "the jintleman that pays the rint", he is in northern lands the mainstay of the poor. Sows are prolific and pigs fatten on less food per pound of weight gained than sheep or cattle. The pig gives fat (now admitted to be full of rich vitamins) to stave off winter cold. Above all, the pig gives savour to whatever is cooked, a virtue our dieticians overlooked in war-time.

A BRITISH BOAR
Etching by Thomas Landseer after Edwin Landseer, 1818

THE ROYAL AGRICULTURAL SOCIETY'S FIRST SHOW, HELD AT OXFORD IN 1839
Lithograph after W. A. De la Motte

It is not surprising therefore that our colder counties gave rise to special breeds. The Large White and Middle White come from Yorkshire, the Tamworth from the cold north Midlands and the Lincolnshire curly-coated from where the bitter east wind blows. A hundred years ago, in 1848, when the Royal Show was held at York, the first Large Whites appeared, having been brought to their high standard by Yorkshire weavers, chief among whom was Joseph Tuley. There was the same inherent skill in these men as in the great cattle-breeders. Other pigs had small peasant origins, such as Wessex, Large White Lop-Ears from Devon, Gloucester Old Spots from the Marches; Wales and Cumberland alike produced their cottage breeds. Pig and cottager are inseparable. In the hungry days of England, Cobbett wrote: "A couple of flitches of bacon are worth fifty thousand Methodist sermons and religious tracts. . . . They are great softeners of the temper and promoters of domestic harmony."

Thus the world's bacon factories are filled with animals developed by men who needed to have many qualities available in the citizens of their sties which were also the rangers of woods and stubbles. In Scandinavia our "between-wars" breakfast bacon came from our own Large White crossed on to native pigs like the Land-Race. Large Black, Tamworth,

31

THE SPOTTISWOODE OX
Mezzotint by James Ward after Alexander Nasmyth, 1804

Wessex and Large White are world parents and still are represented in our meagre imported bacon ration; once, too, there was a time when Berkshire and Middle White returned to us as imported pork. This brings us back to milk, for the foreign dairy products that came with our bacon and eggs are part of one economy. Skim milk and whey—the by-products of butter and cheese—are the complementary protein foods to make bacon or to encourage hens to lay.

Up till now we have only dealt in passing with breeds such as the Red Poll and Shorthorn which developed milking strains from general beef and draught origin. In this class also stand the great, placid South Devon cattle, both larger in frame and lighter in colour than their deep red "up-county" neighbours. Although the Shorthorn is by far the commonest cow in our dairies, and some individuals of the breed like the great cow belonging to Mr. Burge of Itchen Down in Hampshire have given yields of 2,000 gallons in a year more than once, they are specifically considered by their supporters as a dual-purpose breed.

There are only four breeds in the British Isles which originated for the dairy first and foremost: these are Jerseys, Guernseys, Ayrshires and British

WILD WHITE CATTLE IN CHILLINGHAM PARK, NORTHUMBERLAND
Coloured lithograph by Hullmandel and Walton after John Wray Snow, *c.* 1840

Friesians. Thus Ayrshires are the only breed truly indigenous to our main island. The Channel Islanders, as might be expected from their seclusion, have developed with greater specialisation than the rest. Among the western cattle they are the best butter-fat producers. A Jersey cow was the first animal under official test to yield her own weight of butter fat in one year. Jerseys are also famed for their longevity. The Guernsey is only second to the Jersey as a butter-fat producer and being a heavier animal tends to yield rather more milk. Both are intensely domesticated as for centuries they have almost "lived in" with the family. When they came to the mainland at first they were considered the rich man's home-farm hobby. Their opulent yellow milk and delicate, almost deerlike beauty, tended towards this verdict. But in fact they have spread far across the world and endured very rugged conditions. In the Channel Islands great care is taken to keep out tuberculosis. Such is their influence that a great many people consider that yellow milk must be better than white milk and in fact there are regulations against putting colouring matter into milk. Curiously enough, the two other dairy breeds give comparatively white milk, yet of a composition peculiarly suited to the infant stomach.

As early as the seventeenth century Friesians were imported from the Netherlands to East Anglia, owing to the influence of Flemish weavers and Dutch drainage experts. Later, in spite of varied fortunes, British Friesians with mighty frames were to become one of our most spectacular milking breeds, although the British Friesian Society only came into existence in 1909. The British Friesians have been condemned, often unjustly, as giving milk poor in butter fat, for they went through a period when milk yields tended to outweigh quality in this breed. But the breeders have since made great and successful efforts to breed better yielders of butter fat, and what is equally if not more important, a higher total solid content. If criticism can be brought against the Friesian it is that their great frames demand much food to support them before the farmer can start feeding for milk yield. But this is a controversy best left to the breeders themselves.

The Ayrshire stands last, but by no means least on our list. For many generations the Ayrshire type has been established in South-West Scotland. For centuries it had to stand wet and cold, hill-land and lowland conditions and generally lean living. The result has been a medium-sized, neat animal of most prepotent type which ranges for its food, is hardy and breeds regularly and generally yields consistently well with a higher than average butter-fat content. Like many an enterprising Scot, the Ayrshire has done well south of the Border, where it has justified itself as the poor man's cow. Their graceful lyre horns and symmetrical brown and white bodies dapple many pastures in England and abroad.

Although milk recording was advocated as early as 1829, mainly through John Speir of Burn Farm, Dalsy, Ayrshire, the Royal Highland and Agricultural Society of Scotland gave a grant in 1903 from which started three milk-recording societies in Ayrshire, Wigtownshire and Kirkcudbrightshire. Butter-fat tests too were made every 22 days. Speir also introduced tuberculin tests through Professor Bang of Denmark. To-day twenty per cent of Scottish herds are recorded and the practice is growing rapidly throughout Britain. It says much both for Speir's foresight and the healthiness of the Ayrshire cattle that the largest district of disease-free attested cattle is in South-West Scotland.

A hundred years ago it was beef that mattered most and the great improvers founded the Smithfield Club (1799) for fat stock, the Royal Bath and West Show (1780) and the Royal Show (1839), which brought together not only the best animals of the country, but the latest improvements in technique and machinery. Indeed, the growth of our great Shows has gone hand in hand with agricultural improvement, although there were moments when one was tempted to think that the fixing of certain fancy standards in the exhibition of livestock tended to make breeders overlook the more urgent realities of genetics. One thing, however, is certain, that they punctuate our summers throughout the country with a

AN OLD DROVEWAY : EVENING

Water colour by David Cox, 1783-1859

lively interest for all countrymen and an ever-increasing interest for towns-
men since the war, for in spite of petrol and transport difficulties, recent
attendances at the Royal Show and others have broken all previous records
by many thousands. As our rations are short, so is the townsman's interest
in the land increased.

Among the most famous Shows not named above are the Royal Highland, the Royal Welsh, the Royal Counties (home counties and Wiltshire),
the Three Counties (Gloucestershire, Herefordshire and Worcestershire),
the Royal Cornwall, the Royal Lancashire and the Dairy Show. At the
National Dairy Show it has often been possible not only to see the animals
on the hoof, but in the case of pigs to see the animal in carcase and to be
able to judge the accuracy of the "eyes and hands verdict" on the hoof
as compared with the final criterion of the carcase.

Some of these Shows last for two, three and four days. The very prefix
"Royal" attests the interest of His Majesty and his predecessors in farming
and stock breeding and it reflects their importance to the nation, despite
the nation's overwhelmingly industrial character. Many of the most notable
prize-winners have come from the Royal farms at Windsor, Sandringham
and the Duchy of Cornwall. Indeed, when drinking His Majesty's health,
he is often accurately as well as loyally referred to at country gatherings
as "the first farmer in the land".

To win a prize at the Royal, or the National Dairy Show, to name
but two, gives breeders a *cachet* almost impossible to get from other sources.
Both the Royal Agricultural Society of England and the Bath and West
extend activities much further than promoting exhibitions of stock and
machinery: they institute research work as well and medals are given for
new improvements.

The livestock exhibited goes beyond sheep, cattle and horses: it en-
courages the useful goat and is as important to the poultryman as it is to
the large stock-breeder. The pigeon-fancier and the backyard rabbit-
breeder likewise have their niche and, if it is impossible to exhibit bees
and attach rosettes to the Queen, the product of these important little
people and methods of keeping them are by no means forgotten. Only
now, as orchards increase and we have to breed more and more of our own
grass seed, are the agricultural pundits stressing the vital need of enough
of this small livestock on the farm. The Ministry of Agriculture also has
a stand, concerned generally with animal health and fodder crops.

But, if the great Shows are spectacular in their exhibits and the atten-
dance of "very important people", it is often the little Shows scattered
through the Shires which do most to encourage breed improvement and
healthy rivalry among the average farmers of our country. Gathered here
and there for a day, they can discuss their neighbours' stock and see how
far short their own falls in comparison with their more successful rivals
(reluctant as they may be to admit it by word of mouth). Very often these

CATTLE AND SHEEP IN THE CALEDONIAN MARKET
Oil painting by an unknown artist, *c.* 1860

lesser Agricultural Societies are coupled with competitions for the herd or flock as well as for the individual animal shown in the ring.

Here also the farm men gather and sharpen their wits and use their critical faculties among their colleagues from other farms, for, next to the ploughing match, there are few busmen's holidays so much looked forward to among the workers as the local or county Show. Often the herdsman or shepherd receives a card of merit for his good share in the winning of herd and flock competitions.

It is a heartening thing that after the twenty years of depression between the wars, the small and very often respectably ancient Agricultural Societies are having a great revival, with an increased value to the countryside as well as a more stable income.

Almost as an offshoot of the Agricultural Show as such, certain markets have developed as shows in themselves, including the Christmas fat stock shows which are really sales with prizes for the best entries. Many a butcher in the happy days gone by has been pleased to boast the carcase of magnificent meat with the prize rosette attached in his window for the Christmas shopper. In other places the Auction Marts have developed pedigree sales, again with prizes for the best entries of genuine animals conforming to a strict breed test and often to stringent regulations for freedom from disease.

Slowly the emphasis has changed from beef to dairy animals. Throughout the great agricultural depression which surged and subsided, but always flowed with the economic tide from the late '70's until 1939, milk selling gradually became the earner of weekly wage cheques on many of our farms. From the Dorset vales, beloved of Hardy, where milk had always been the mainstay and Tess of the D'Urbervilles' occupation was traditional, the milk cow spread to wherever there was water. Thus by 1925, 838 million gallons were sold to the public in England and Wales; by 1946 it had increased to 1,259 million gallons. Now, with the high cost of imported dairy products, if we are to make enough butter and cheese, or even to keep pace with the rising demand for liquid milk, we shall need more milk than ever. Have we the animals and have we sufficient land to go on increasing our herds? With modern technique in grass management we could carry well over 4 million dairy cows—approximately 25 per cent more than to-day. It is hard to disentangle the number of cows kept as commercial producers from the sum total of cattle listed in the Ministry of Agriculture's Annual Returns. But if we exclude all heifers in calf, the number of cows and heifers in milk and dry cows in calf (June 1949) is probably over 3,600,000 in the U.K. This figure may well include some animals that are not strictly milk producers (in the dairy-farming sense).

This vast supply of fresh milk needed to-day demands health in our animals and hygiene in our methods. Great strides are being taken in the pathological treatment of our animals and in precautionary measures like tuberculin testing and immunisation against abortion. But the future will depend upon how we go about the task of breeding and feeding animals and finding men to tend them.

CATTLE MARKET AT MELTON MOWBRAY
Oil painting by John Ferneley, 1853

37

BRITISH LIVESTOCK TO-DAY AND TO-MORROW

THE reputation of our livestock was born in the heyday of English farming and maintained through the depression by a body of pedigree breeders whose methods tended away from the agricultural average of depression days. The breeders for the most part maintained the nineteenth-century canons of good husbandry, relying on sums from pedigree stock sold at home and abroad to overcome possible losses on their crops. Naturally, there have been casualties among them. The heavy horse breeder often has to fight a losing battle, for tractor and motor are ousting horses everywhere in the world where prices are high and labour is scarce.

At first the tendency of the mechanised farmer was to obliterate livestock, beginning with the horse; he concentrated with labour-saving methods on continuous cash crops. Specialisation became the order of the day, for on commercial stock farms the other extremity obtained, where the plough was almost unknown and animals were used as a processing factory for foodstuffs obtained from overseas. In the very nature of things, such establishments could not bother with breed improvement, always till now the sphere of the artist farmer, rather than the average farmer. There were, however, some highly specialised commercial pig and poultry breeding farms.

However, the 1939-45 war intervened and brought to a head what peace-time events were already shaping. Many pioneers of arable mechanisation had begun to turn towards stock to balance the loss of humus in their soil. Disease had already begun to show itself in the specialised stock farms. It had become obvious in the intensive egg farm; less obvious, but still discernible, in the far more widespread ploughless dairy farm. In the meantime, the work of Sir George Stapledon and his colleagues on improved rotation grasses pointed the way to a livestock-cum-arable revival. Grass has always been and is still our most important crop.

By cutting off nearly all imported feeding stuffs the war turned a trend into an agricultural revolution. We needed corn and milk. The stock farms were ploughed again, and mixed farming came into its own. The need for milk actually increased our dairy cattle. But beef herds waned and sheep declined (the latter mainly on account of labour difficulties). In many instances poultry flocks and whole herds of pigs completely disappeared. This happened especially in cases where they had before been entirely dependent on imported food.

Now that phase is over. For years it is probable that we shall not be able to import enough animal feeding stuffs. But war has accelerated the consumption of animal products everywhere. In South America, the Argentine is the only country with an exportable surplus of meat. Eggs, bacon and mutton are everywhere in demand at high prices. At the same time we in England, who cannot afford the exports to pay for high-priced animal

HEREFORD BULL
Oil painting by James Ward, 1769–1859

products from overseas, are sorely in need of them. In other words, we have reached a point where we must gradually turn from the survival farming of the war to intensive mixed farming in which livestock is the pivot.

Taken as a whole, after ten years of war-time farming, we need to restore fertility with stock and grass. The nutritionist tells us we need all the livestock products we can get to maintain health. When it is available, the cheapest and easiest of all things to import is cereals, such as wheat, maize and barley. It costs just twice as much in foreign currency to import bacon or eggs as to import the equivalent amount in cereals to produce the same bacon and eggs at home. A mixed livestock policy marries itself to good husbandry, nutritional needs and sane economy of imports.

As always, cattle will be the mainstay of livestock farming. Of these dairy cattle must preponderate, to give us milk, cheese and butter. And here lies our greatest need for improvement. Dairy Shorthorn, Channel Islander, Ayrshire, Red Poll, Lincolnshire Red Shorthorn and home-bred Friesians have all built up an international demand. The demand may well persist, especially in countries where the indigenous cattle are much in need of improvement. However, the Brown Swiss, Dutch and South African Friesians will be strong competitors. Canada and the U.S.A. have built up great dairy strains, so that they consider their own stock equal, if not superior, to our best. Probably export of our dairy breeds to the Western Hemisphere will decline for some time to come. Whether intensive concentration on one set of qualities, that is, yield of milk and butter fat, will ultimately cause a decline of stamina in North American herds, has yet to be seen. It may well be that, if we pursue a breeding policy based on consistent fair yields, persistent fertility and longevity, once again there will be a Western market open to us.

A new factor will probably militate against the bodily export of cattle. Artificial insemination seems to offer so many advantages at the moment that the export of semen by air may well replace export of most bulls, and that one bull may be used to perform the work once done by twenty or more of his colleagues. This is the modern trend, which for good or ill appears to be developing. Whether Nature will ultimately turn on those who so desire to short-circuit her wisdom is something we shall not be able to tell for many years to come. At present those who think they can replace Nature's methods are very sure of their success. Thus, our main opportunity will be to improve the somewhat indifferent average cattle of Great Britain.

Recorded yields of milk depend so much on environment that it is not always easy to disentangle environment from inheritance. Again, breeders' sale catalogues too often lay emphasis on individual performances among the forebears of the animal advertised for sale; the family failures on the side of sire or dam are discreetly omitted, even where they are known. For a long period our show system tended to over-emphasise external conformation of stock; sometimes unnecessary attention has been given to fancy points of body markings. However, recent rules for exhibition of stock at Shows are setting a far higher all-round standard.

If we are to expand as a great and economical dairy country, three main improvements will have to take place. First and foremost there is the

JERSEY BULL
Oil painting by Juliet McLeod, 1946

education of milk producer and stockman in good animal management. We can no longer rely on large quantities of imported feeding stuffs, exotic foods with which to cram long-suffering animals. This may be all to the good. Good grass, good hay and silage, ultimately perhaps good dried grass as well, will have to replace most of the concentrates we used to feed, to obtain milk over and above the first gallon from our average "Heinz variety" herds. This should improve our cattle's health. Better milking methods and more natural living conditions help much. By these means alone our total yields could improve by at least one hundred gallons per cow or say 3–400,000,000 gallons a year. Like everything else concerned in farming, this is a gradual but by no means impossible process.

The second method is by universal use of improved sires. Here lies the great opportunity of our pedigree breeders. We will have to use many more old bulls whose worth is already proven by their progeny; that is, bulls of five years old and over. The commercial practice of using any male of passable conformation, perhaps known to have come of a fair yielding dam, merely as a means of getting a cow ready for another lactation, is disappearing. We will need sufficient dairy bulls whose inherited qualities, when used on our dairy cows, will be capable of increasing yields of the daughter by a hundred gallons a year as compared with dams giving the national average of to-day. This would give a resultant increase of yield equal to that already quoted in connection with improved methods of management. As management improves all round, so it will be possible more closely to assess improvement through inheritance. Also the ordinary farmer should be encouraged to hold to a consistent breeding policy. Thus the writer believes that we should aim at a national average yield of seven to eight hundred gallons per cow. Owing to lack of feeding stuffs, the national average yield per cow has slightly declined since 1939. The present figure is estimated to be 567 gallons (1948–49). In Denmark, where efforts have been intensified for eighty years, the recorded average yield per cow was 800 gallons in 1938–39. This increase would nearly equal the total quantity sold to the public of England and Wales in 1945. That should be done by bringing up the poor yield of the average and less than average herd, rather than by greatly increasing the yield of the better herds. The milk cow is a very sensitive animal and aiming at too high an average yield is almost certain to end with short life, sterility and loss of stamina.

The third method is the elimination of most of our diseases. Our veterinary surgeons are already making great efforts in prophylaxis and the early weeding-out of diseased animals by testing and herd inspection. At the same time all this work is accompanied by constant teaching of better animal hygiene and care of young stock. Before 1939 it was reckoned that ascertainable disease cost the farmer about £14,000,000 a year; at to-day's prices this sum could easily be doubled. But the cost of sub-normality in animal health is probably greater than that caused by disease in recognised pathological forms. It is here that future improvement lies far more in the hands of the farmer and the expert breeder than in the hands of the "vet". This could be true even if all our herds were raised to the "attested standard" in freedom from pathological disease.

Really sound farming and breeding makes all the difference to animals forced to live such an artificial life as the dairy cow. "Taking the plough round the farm" so that there is plenty of fresh pasture for feed, the use of home-grown, high-quality fodders, keeping animals in fresh air as much as possible and with good water supply, are better than "an apple a day to keep the doctor away".

To rear heifer calves we should try to suckle them on nurse cows for the first eight weeks. The experimental work of the Cornish County Agricultural Committee has shown this to be not only desirable, but economical. If the farmer can be assured that the bull he buys comes from a family in which the females on both sides have averaged, say, seven

By courtesy of Walker's (

SOW AND PIGLETS

Coloured engraving after J. F. Herring senior, 1855

calves in eight or nine years and have given a mean yield of 900 gallons a year at about 4 per cent butter fat, he knows he is breeding for stamina and fertility as much as yield.

The average yield per cow-life is far more important than yield per lactation. For almost the first three years of life the cow is eating up crops and pasture before she yields anything in return. In fact she has probably consumed one season's produce off several acres in that time. To-day her average milking life is about three lactations. There is no reason, with good breeding and management, why that should not be doubled. The saving would be as follows. As we have seen, we could carry a population of well over 4,000,000 dairy cows (exclusive of heifers in calf). If these last for three lactations, we need over 3,000,000 female calves and store heifers coming on merely to replace them. If these cows gave six lactations we would only need about a million and a half young cattle as replacements. Thus the produce of well over a million acres of our soil could be freed for other purposes. We have dwelt upon the problems of dairy stock at some length, partly because it is our most important problem and partly because so many of these considerations apply to all animal husbandry. There is no doubt that, if these improvements which we need so badly could come about in fifteen years, we would be the leading dairy country of the world, producing much fine cheese and butter as well as milk.

It would be fruitless here to enter into the controversy of dual-purpose versus pure dairy breed. The writer himself believes the controversy will gradually die out if the policy of dairy stock improvement outlined above takes place. The animal capable of sustained fertility and long, steady-yielding life will inevitably make a better carcase for the butcher and her steer calves should fatten into fair meat once the butcher's prejudice about outer markings has disappeared. It is your thriftless dairy cow which produces thriftless calves. Moreover, if cows can be made to live for six lactations and more, we can afford to put beef bulls on half of our dairy cows and so produce about 1,500,000 more good beef calves a year.

One role of our pure beef herds will be to supply bulls both for home and export trade. Although artificial insemination may affect the export trade, one cannot help but feel that the beef animals of Britain are in a stronger position for overseas demand than our dairy animals. They were specifically bred before milk assumed its modern importance. Wherever new land is to be developed, beef comes first; wherever living conditions improve, it is beef that is eaten in increasing quantities. Finally, the shortcomings of soil show very soon in beef and therefore the great beef-renewing qualities of British stock are most needed. Good beef comes from good conformation first and foremost. British breeders and soil excel in producing this.

At home there is bound to be a strong demand for first-rate stores to fatten in the great arable districts like East Anglia. Once the making of good dung is successfully mechanised, winter fattening of beef will return

43

CHAMPION SHIRE STALLION, 'ALTHORPE TRUMP CARD'
Charcoal drawing by Juliet McLeod, 1948

to the lands which have too greatly relied on artificial methods of restoring fertility without humus to the soil. On any farm, beef stores leave more fertility to the farmer than milk cows, which take an undue quantity of phosphate and lime from the ground.

Sheep, pigs and chickens are still badly needed. They are also the complement to cattle in livestock husbandry. Varied grazing means good use of grass; few animals will eat close to where they have left their own droppings or urine, but horses will graze after cattle and sheep after both. Their different methods of grazing mean also that they will attack all useful grasses equally and so grass will be fully utilised. Sheep are the great scavengers of a mixed farm. Any crops, root, hay, grass or stubble can be utilised by sheep when cattle do not need them. To farm for cattle one must always have a margin of crops left over which sheep can use. Just as some parts of Britain are ideally suited to raise beef stores for fattening elsewhere, so many hill lands are ideally suited to raise sheep which can be drafted on to lowland farms which need them. As we have seen, this interchange is centuries old. Beef cattle are also bred as stores in the hills and sold to the valleys for fattening. Indeed, the Government has recognised the value of hill farms by giving special subsidies for hill sheep and cattle.

CHAMPION SUFFOLK PUNCH STALLION, 'NAUNTON PRINCE'
Charcoal drawing by Juliet McLeod, 1947

Sheep will be needed for meat and wool and for their complementary part in husbandry. Many will say there are too many breeds. Certain it is that there are far too many hotch-potch flocks in the land, random-bred from lots bought here, there and everywhere. Our best sheep are known the world over—both Down sheep and hill breeds. The Brave New World loves a safe sameness—every man in store trousers, every ounce of processed cheese the same. Standardisation is the order of the day. But you cannot standardise hills and valleys, soils and climates. Some of the lesser-known breeds may disappear, yet there must always be variety to suit the land, and the skill of the ordinary lowland farmer will lie in finding crosses suitable for his land, which will grow into good, gradable mutton and wool. He will probably continue to return to the hills for his breeding ewes and to the great Down flocks for his sires.

It is however most unlikely that the arable breeds will live mainly in folds as they have before. These breeds grew up to meet the demands of improved agriculture a hundred and fifty years ago. Their sheepfolds followed the plough because in the Norfolk four-course rotation they brought fertility and the mechanical consolidation of the "Golden Hoof" to the light soil. Although it was good farming, it was not the only way,

45

nor necessarily the best for the sheep themselves. Arable folds of roots in a wet winter and early lambing are not the most natural ways of sheep-keeping. The Down breeds thrive on grass like any other cattle. Thus they have thriven abroad and thus will probably thrive in England over all the country as they graze after cattle on rotation grasses.

Here it is necessary to make a digression. In the '20's our competitors based their exports to us on standardisation. Danish bacon, Canterbury lamb and Argentine chilled meat came to us of excellent quality and uniform joints. Thus one could see a hundred sides of bacon all looking as if they were cut from one model pig. The misfits, the odd sizes and qualities were consumed at home. Therefore British consumers were the most spoiled public in the world as regards standardisation. By various means like the National Mark for home-killed beef, and the Pig and Bacon Boards, equal and sometimes higher standards were set for the home producer. Therefore the breeders themselves reacted to the standard demand and because the size of families decreased the demand for small joints made for smaller animals and earlier maturity among sheep and cattle breeds. Standardisation done purely for the consumer may lead to doubtful breeding. Thus the fine-shouldered pig which the bacon factories required might tempt the breeder to produce an animal whose constitution would be weakened. Too much attention to early maturity might also end in sacrificing other good qualities.

The fact that we can afford to waste no animal products may mean that the consumer will continue for many years to be less exacting by far than in 1939. Thus while breeders should always work for the highest quality, the risk of breeding solely for the fancies of the public, which pre-war competition enforced, should be greatly lessened.

Pigs present an immediate problem, because we have to feed them mainly on cereals which are in demand for direct human consumption, or are hard to get from abroad. There is another difficulty in that, for some time to come, nearly all our milk will be used for human consumption. When pig food is short nothing is so useful as skim milk to supply quality in the ration. This is the foundation of farm economy in Scandinavia and elsewhere.

Therefore, we will have to forgo our pre-war method of feeding pigs on New World products and will have to use a variety of methods to increase our present miserably small pig population. The pig is necessary because almost the whole of his carcase is useful for meat, leather, bristles, bone, etc. He has a larger proportion of edible and highly nutritious offal than any other animal and scientists at last proclaim him high in valuable vitamins.

To meet this need we will have to fall back on a multitude of producers rather than the specialised commercial pig farm of the past. There is hardly a farm in the country that cannot breed, or at least feed, a few

SHORTHORN BULL
Pencil drawing by C. F. Tunnicliffe, 1944

pigs. For the good of his soil every market gardener should keep some pigs or chickens. Now pigs can live on grass or vegetable waste so as to replace at least 2lb. a head of the grain ration. Potatoes, of which we should always have a large margin, are excellent pig food, provided there is some high protein like fish meal or bean meal. If we had skim milk the whole rations could be found on almost any farm.

Thus, the more good cows we have, the more surplus milk can be turned to butter-making, and the more beef we kill the easier it will be to keep pigs on the waste animal products. The larger mixed farms should be able to grow their own grain to keep up good-quality, pure-bred pigs as foundation stock for the little man.

Now, if our farming future is to be based on an intensification of live-stock as opportunity arises and skill permits, who will tend them? Cows have to be milked Sundays and weekdays. Poultry and pigs must be tended Sundays and weekdays and sheep at all times during lambing. Mixed farms fully stocked need many more workers than a pure arable farm. Our land carrying a full quota of stock and intensively farmed may well demand half a million more workers. Many of us contend that this would be a social benefit to the nation. In the world of mass production of human minds as well as goods, the more people who can live a whole, healthy, individually creative life the better.

But life in our industrial world has become fragmented; work is divorced from leisure and the general temper of our times inevitably affects the countryside. So to get our new stockmen, conditions will have to be created where regular leisure times can be arranged and conditions are such that the womenfolk willingly live on the land. This is not the place to argue in detail how a return to the land depends mainly on the women. Yet it is true that without their happy assent we cannot repopulate the countryside. The life of the stockman must therefore especially appeal to his wife. This is a most difficult problem, for after you have solved the question of good housing and amenities such as lighting and sewage and water and schooling and a good life of neighbourhood, the stockman's hours and his need to dwell close to his stock may still set his wife or fiancée against his chosen profession, although he is better paid than most of his neighbours and well honoured, if he is at the head of his profession. There will probably be enough families to live close to key jobs even in isolated districts, but better transport and good roads will help, more especially if there is a full life in the neighbourhood and varied opportunity for the children.

Among the larger farmers a solution can be found by training tractor drivers or general farm workers as milkers, shepherds, stock-feeders and so forth who can replace in regular rotation the permanent stockmen who wish for well-earned times off or who may fall sick. It is well worth paying a farm worker a weekly cash bonus, if he is willing and able to look after sheep or pigs or milk in turn to give the regular stockmen time to shop, play football or be with their families like other farm hands. A system of teaching men to be spare-time milkers, shepherds, pig and poultrymen as part of their farm training, and which would yield proficiency pay analogous to proficiency pay in the Services, would be one of the greatest advances we could make.

Among the family farmers the first lesson in co-operation is to learn to help in tending neighbours' stock so that the seven-day week may be mitigated for all. A fresh vision is demanded and the will to implement it in education and among the farmers is required to provide the stockman of the future. There are still no strikes or absentees in our hard-pressed farming community, but we need a continuing positive effort to make life as full and rich for all (including the wives) who serve the land, as it can be for those whose all-absorbing vocation it is.

The stockman's is the most responsible of all farming work; it breeds character as it has always done. It is necessary to the nation's soul as well as its stomach, for the greatest crop the land can yield is desirable and happy human beings.

BRITISH BREEDS OF LIVESTOCK

As Listed in the Ministry of Agriculture's Bulletin No. 86 (now out of print).

CATTLE

BEEF CATTLE

SHORTHORN ⎫
SUSSEX   ⎬ English
HEREFORD ⎪
DEVON   ⎭
ABERDEEN ANGUS
WEST HIGHLAND
GALLOWAY (used in N. England)
BELTED GALLOWAY (used mainly in Northumberland, Cumberland, S.W. Scotland)

DUAL-PURPOSE CATTLE

SOME STRAINS OF SHORTHORNS
LINCOLNSHIRE RED SHORTHORN
RED POLL
SOUTH DEVON
WELSH BLACK
LONGHORN
DEXTER (imported from Ireland, 1886)
PARK CATTLE (direct descendants of old wild white bulls)

DAIRY CATTLE

DAIRY SHORTHORN
AYRSHIRE
JERSEY
GUERNSEY
BRITISH FRIESIAN
KERRY (from Eire)
BLUE ALBION

OTHERS

OLD GLOUCESTERSHIRE
SHETLAND

SHEEP

LONG-WOOLLED AND MOUNTAIN BREEDS

LEICESTER
BORDER LEICESTER
LINCOLN
ROMNEY MARSH
WENSLEYDALE
SOUTH DEVON
DEVON LONGWOOL
DEVON CLOSEWOOL
SHETLAND
SCOTCH BLACKFACE
LONK (Lancashire)
DERBYSHIRE
GRITSTONE
ROUGH FELL
SWALEDALE
LIMESTONE
PENISTONE
CHEVIOT
WELSH MOUNTAIN
RADNOR
HERDWICK (Fell districts only)
EXMOOR HORN (or Porlock)
DARTMOOR

DOWN BREEDS

SOUTHDOWN
SHROPSHIRE
CLUN
SUFFOLK
HAMPSHIRE
OXFORD
DORSET
DORSET HORN
KERRY HILL (from Wales)
RYELAND (Herefordshire)
WILTSHIRE HORN

HORSES	PIGS
DRAUGHT	BERKSHIRE
	CUMBERLAND
SHIRE	WHITE-SHOULDERED ESSEX
CLYDESDALE (used fairly extensively	GLOUCESTERSHIRE OLD SPOTS
in N. England)	(known as Cottage Pig)
SUFFOLK	LARGE BLACK PIG
PERCHERON (imported from France,	LARGE WHITE PIG
1916)	(or Large White Yorkshire)
	LARGE WHITE ULSTER
LIGHTS	LONG WHITE LOP-EARED PIG
	('White Lop' or 'Lop White')
CLEVELAND BAY	MIDDLE WHITE
DALES PONY	TAMWORTH
DARTMOOR PONY	WELSH
EXMOOR PONY	WESSEX SADDLEBACK
FELL PONY	
HACKNEY	
NEW FOREST PONY	
HUNTER (mixed breed)	
SHETLAND PONY (used in N. Eng-	
land coalfields)	
THOROUGHBRED (mixed origin)	
WELSH PONY AND COB